FRUIT HAPPENS!

a story by **Michael Christopher**

Fruit Happens!

Cover design by KristinPaulDesign.com
Interior layout by StandingPixels.com

This book made available without charge by The 1687 Foundation, a nonprofit, tax-exempt organization dedicated to advancing spiritual and charitable purposes. Please note that these books may only be given away. They cannot be sold, cannot be used to raise money, and cannot be a "free giveaway" for any commercial or personal-gain purpose whatsoever.

The 1687 Foundation First Printing, 2010
Printed in the United States of America

For additional information, please contact:
info@1687foundation.com
Tel: 541.549.7600
Fax: 541.549.7603

By their fruits ye shall know them.
(Matthew 7:20)

Contents

A Word from Dellie

If you've never read a book called *Dellie O'Shea* you won't know much about me. So maybe I'd better introduce myself.

My birth name was Delbert Stevens but I've been called Dellie O'Shea most of my life. I was born in 1885. I grew up in Connecticut but I spent many years in Missouri. Plus a few other states along the way.

During much of that time I was a singer and a dancer, although I found myself in the middle of a lot of other adventures, too. Like robbery, kidnapping, and things even worse than that. But I was always on the right side of the law even though I sometimes had to dance pretty fast to stay there.

Two more things you ought to know. First, I wasn't much of a Christian during most of those adventures. But I should have been, because when the story I'm about to tell you popped back into my memory, many years after it happened, it made me remember once again that God had been watching out for me for a long time. He'd never stopped giving me lessons on what He was all about, even though I didn't always pay attention.

I'm hoping you will.

Finally, I really didn't want to mention this but somewhere along the line you've got to know it. I am what people used to call a "midget." Nowadays they'd call me a "little person," but to me it's all the same. At my very tallest I was never more than thirty-seven inches high, and never weighed more than sixty-five pounds.

In many ways, physical size doesn't matter one bit. On the other hand it might have had something to do with part of the story I want to tell you in the next few pages.

THE BASEBALL GAME

CHAPTER 1

We were playing baseball in the field down the road from my house. By "we" I mean Jamie Goldstein and me, plus four other guys. Until a girl showed up.

Her name was Paisley Baker so most of us called her "Cake." But that wasn't what made her special. She could throw a baseball farther than most of the guys, and none of us could catch her on the bases.

Cake wanted to play too, but since the sides were even she had to wait until somebody else showed up so we could add one player to each team. It didn't take very long.

His name was Billy Page. Most of our parents wanted us to call him "Mister" because he was older than some of them, but we were never able to do it. Much of the time Billy acted like he was a kid, just like the rest of us.

He also had a son named Harry, who was pitching for the other team that day. So we put Billy on my side and sent Cake out to cover the infield.

Harry Page absolutely hated Cake Baker and used to make fun of her in more ways than you could count. And it wasn't just nasty faces and wiseguy names—he was full of dirty tricks and other mean things, including that absolute classic. He once dipped one of her braids in a bottle of ink.

So, putting Cake Baker out there just a few feet away from him was a little risky. You could see it in the look of disgust on his face. I think he also made a few smart-aleck remarks under his breath, but none of us could hear him for sure. Cake didn't seem to mind one way or the other.

When my next turn to bat came I hit an easy grounder to Cake and she threw the ball to Harry to force me out. Pretty routine stuff. What happened next was not.

When Billy Page came up it was a case of father against son, so most of us paid a little more attention than usual. Because he was so much older and bigger, Billy could hit the ball a lot farther than the rest of us. Usually, whenever he played with us he took it easy, but for some reason I think he really swung hard this time.

He missed the first pitch by a mile. That made him look foolish and might have made him swing even harder the next time. On the second pitch he connected with a loud crack and sent a vicious line drive straight back toward the pitcher. Harry never had a chance. Before he could even raise his glove the ball hit him square in the face, with a sickening smack that sounded like a water balloon crashing into a tree.

I don't think I've seen such an instant collapse any other time in my life. Harry went down without making a sound. I thought he was dead for sure, but like everyone else I ran full speed, hoping against hope, to where Harry lay in the grass, flat on his back.

Cake Baker got there first. She lifted his head up and tried to talk to him. "Harry! Harry! Wake up! Are you all right? Wake up!"

One of the other guys grabbed a bottle of water and shook some in Harry's face, but that didn't do any good. His nose already looked about twice as wide as usual, and the water just smeared the blood around a little more. I think that some of Harry's teeth were knocked loose, too. His mouth was wide open. I don't think much air was getting through his nose.

By then, Billy Page had taken charge. We watched him pick his son up and carry him across the road to his front yard, holding up his head the best he could while he half-ran and half-walked. Cake and I followed him and sat on the lawn, so Billy could lay Harry between us while he hitched up two horses to his carriage. Cake put Harry's head in her lap, in spite of all the blood, and held a big towel up to his face. As soon as Billy was ready we loaded him in on the seat and took off for Dr. Bassano's house.

I'm not sure but I think Billy Page was crying by the time we got there. "I didn't mean to hurt him. I didn't mean to hurt him!" was all he could say. Lucky for us he didn't run over anybody on the way. The doctor lived halfway across town, so Billy had to guide the horses through quite a bit of traffic, using eyes that were not very clear.

By the time we got him through the front door, Harry was moving his hands again so we knew he was still alive. The doctor's wife took us straight into one of the side rooms, where his father laid Harry on one of those big old examination platforms that look like a cross between a plastic bed and a padded table. Doctor Bassano came in almost instantly and tried to shoo all three of us out of the room.

"But I'm his father!" said Billy.

"All right, all right—you can stay. Just stand over there while I see what's going on."

That's all Cake and I knew for the next thirty minutes or so, until Billy Page came out and sat down beside us in the front room.

"They threw me out too," he said. "They have to stop the bleeding and put his nose back together, but they've got him breathing okay. Let's just hope he doesn't have a scrambled brain."

CHAPTER 2

After another thirty minutes or so the doctor came out and told us officially that Harry was not about to pass away.

"His nose is broken up pretty bad, and we might need to do some work on the bones in his face, but he should come out of this okay. I don't think we'll see any real neck or brain damage at this point. But it'll take a little while to get him pulled back together."

By that time Harry's mother—who was a block away visiting some friends when all this happened—had also been brought over by one of the neighbors. She was trying very hard not to cry, but when the doctor mentioned brain damage she couldn't hold it back any longer. He paused for a moment and took a long look at her before he lowered his eyes and said any more.

"Ma'am, it's probably better if you don't try to see him for a while. He won't be doing much talking anyway."

Billy finally calmed down enough to look over at me. "Come on, Dellie," he said. "Let me take you and Paisley home. We'll come over later tonight when the doctor is through and we know for sure what's up."

On the way, Billy seemed to relax a little bit. "I want to thank both of you for helping out," he said. "Especially you, Paisley. I don't know how I would have got him there without you to hold him together. Plus, I know how nasty Harry has been to you over the last few months. He doesn't really mean it, you know. I think it's just a boy-girl thing."

By that time Billy was looking sideways at Cake, and he almost smiled. "It's not very often that a girl can throw a ball farther than most boys of the same age," he said. "Or run faster. And I think Harry doesn't quite know how to deal with that."

Cake didn't utter a word at first, but I could see she was fighting a grin of her own. "Harry's not so bad," she finally said, almost under her breath. "He just makes me try harder. But don't tell him that—he's got enough to deal with right now."

Billy was really smiling now. "Oh—I almost forgot! Those clothes of yours could be ruined. That blood won't all come out. Have your mother let me know—at the very least we owe you a new outfit."

I had blood on my own shirt, too, but I guess Billy didn't notice. After he let us out, Cake and I still had to walk a half-block to get to our houses, which were side-by-side on a rocky little dead-end road too narrow for Billy to turn the carriage around in. By then I had a question of my own.

"I still don't think I understand," I finally said. "You had every reason in the world to want to get even with Harry. And after the way he's acted lately a lot of people would have let him bleed to death. But you were the first one to help and the last one to leave. What gives?"

For the first time ever I thought I'd caught Cake Baker with her tongue tied, but not for long. "It's really very simple. But I'm not sure I can explain all by myself. Why don't you come with me tomorrow night?"

"With you where?"

"To Brian Morgan's house. His dad is our Youth Group advisor. Some of the other kids will talk about what we've been learning, and Brian's dad will fill in the gaps."

I'd known for some time that Cake Baker went to church every Sunday, but I hadn't held it against her. At that point I just thought it was something girls did; something I didn't need to do myself unless I got in some horrible trouble I couldn't fix on my own.

So I didn't agree to go with her the next night. But that's not the way it worked out.

DELLIE GOES TO A MEETING

CHAPTER 3

Sometime late in the afternoon of the next day, Cake Baker banged on our front door. I was in the backyard, picking peaches off one of our fruit trees, but I could hear the hollow knocking sound from there. I walked around the house and she started talking before we even said hello.

"My mother just talked to Harry's parents down at the hardware store. They asked her to tell us that Harry should be okay."

"Wow. That's good news! Is he awake?"

"I guess so," Cake continued, "but I think he's in and out right now. They said he woke up in the middle of the night. He has a terrible headache and his nose will never be quite the same, but when the swelling goes down he should look fairly normal again."

"I'm not sure Harry ever did look normal," I said, and we both smiled.

"They said he might have a crack or two in his cheekbones, but those should heal okay."

She stopped for a moment, then continued in a quieter voice. "They also thanked both of us for helping his dad get him to the doctor in one piece. I guess they really appreciate it."

I nodded, and for a moment I thought I saw a tear in Cake's eye. Then she caught her breath and changed the subject.

"So . . . are you going to Brian's house with me tonight?"

For a moment I was confused, but then I remembered. "I guess I hadn't thought much about it," I said, wishing I'd had time to make up a better answer. "I'm not sure I'd fit in."

Cake grinned at me and made one of the few remarks I ever heard from her about my size. "If anyone can fit in, Dellie, that would be you. There's plenty of room, especially for someone who doesn't take up any more than you do! Besides, I think you'll like what's going on—each of the kids has to come up with examples of what one of the 'fruits of the Spirit' looks like in real life. Working it out in our own heads really helps us understand."

I couldn't help looking at the two peaches in my hand. "Here's a fruit for you," I said, handing one to her. "Can't think of a better example than that!"

She grinned slightly and reached out to take it. "Thanks, Dellie. But you know this isn't exactly the kind of fruit I'm talking about."

We didn't say much beyond that, but by the time Cake Baker headed back to her own house I'd agreed to walk over to Brian Morgan's place with her that evening.

She knocked on my front door again, right after supper, and the two of us were soon on our way. By the time we arrived at least six other kids were already there, along with both of Brian's parents. His dad sat in a big chair at the edge of a circle of smaller seats—no doubt at all that he was the leader. Brian's mom bustled around the room, putting out plates of cookies where everyone could reach them and promising lemonade to anyone who might want some.

It took us about twenty minutes to settle in before Mr. Morgan could begin. At that point he looked around the room and nodded at each of us.

"I'm glad to see we have one or two newcomers with us tonight," he finally said. "Dellie and Harvey—good to see both of you! And Monica, too—nice to have all of you, and we hope you enjoy our company so you'll want to come back!"

This all came with a great big smile that seemed a little overdone to me. And for a moment I thought about making a silly joke about Har-Monica, but I managed to keep quiet.

"I see that some of you brought your Bibles, too. So let's turn to the fifth chapter of Galatians and review the Scripture portion before we begin."

He waited at least a full minute while Cake and the others shuffled through their Bibles to find the right place. I didn't have one with me, so all I could do was sit there and feel a little like I was on the spot. Then Mr. Morgan finally began to read.

"But the fruit of the Spirit is love, joy, peace, longsuffering, gentleness, goodness, faith, meekness, temperance: against such there is no law."

He looked around the room. "Okay, everyone. Last week we talked for a while about each of these so-called 'fruits.' Who can tell me what we said this passage actually means? What kind of 'fruits' are we talking about? And why does the Bible use that word right here?"

No one spoke for a minute, but finally one hand went up. "It's not 'fruit' like an apple or a pear, but it is something that grows," said one of the guys.

"Good! But grows how? And where? Does it grow on a tree?"

"Only if the person is like Hank over there!" Cake chimed in.

Hank was not any older than most of us but he was already almost six feet tall. He looked like a fence post with arms, so skinny his bones showed through no matter what he wore. Good thing he didn't mind being laughed at, because that's what happened. But I think everyone knew that Cake was just kidding, including Mr. Morgan.

"Well, I suppose it can seem like that," he finally said. "Hank is just a little bit ahead of the rest of you when it comes to physical growth. But what do you think, Hank— what's a 'fruit of the Spirit,' anyway?"

Hank was still smiling when he answered. "I think it means something that grows naturally, out of who we are."

"That's good, that's good! It takes care of the 'fruit' part. But what does Hank mean when he says 'who we are'?" Mr. Morgan turned to face the rest of the group. "What's the bigger idea here?"

I honestly think that most of the people in the room knew the answer, but it took a while for anyone to put up his hand. Finally, Cake took a chance.

"The 'spirit' part is the spirit of God, living inside us. And when it lives there it changes us. It helps us become more like God Himself."

"Wow! That's a big change! What does she mean by that . . . anyone?"

At that point about six people raised their hands and the conversation raced around the room as fast as each one could finish.

"There's no point in pretending that God is in us if we don't act like it."

"But acting doesn't work—no one can pretend for very long. It has to be real."

"And it can't be real if it's not from God."

"And it can't be from God if we don't ask for it ourselves."

"Which is a big point—He doesn't force anyone to let Him in."

In a way that I couldn't really appreciate until I got a lot older, that short conversation said almost everything that really mattered about God. Mr. Morgan jumped on the last comment immediately.

"So," he said, looking very happy with what was going on, "if we were to sum all this up, would it be fair to say that God loves us, God wants us to love Him, and He also wants us to love others just like He does?"

"That would be pretty close," said Hank. "But the big thing I get from all this is that only God can really help us change ourselves. He won't force Himself into our lives in a real way if we're not willing. So in the end it's like a team thing—a partnership."

That's right," said one of the girls. "And we have to want to be on the same team with God."

Mr. Morgan let his eyes roam around the room with a huge smile on his face. Looking back, I realized later that this little group had just laid out the main message of the Bible in the shortest sermon I'd ever heard. But I wasn't quite ready to understand it yet.

WHERE IT ALL BEGINS

CHAPTER 4

The next item on the group's agenda that night was a case-by-case look at each "fruit of the Spirit." I've already put the original words of the Bible verses in the chapter you just read, but here they are again. Only this time, I've added numbers beside the list of the fruits, and in the discussion that followed.

Also, one more thing you need to know. The original words came from the King James Version of the Bible, which is just about the only one most of us had ever read from in those days. I know there are lots of other translations around today, but in 1898 or so we didn't have much else.

However, in three or four places in the list below I have taken the liberty of using the words that Mr. Morgan and his group actually used during their discussion that night. I think they'd already agreed—probably the week before—on more modern terms that made the text easier for them to understand. After all, the King James Version of the Bible was already almost 300 years old back in the 1890s. Some of those older words sounded terrific but weren't always so clear to younger readers.

So—here are the two verses, from Galatians 5:22–23, laid out like a slightly more modern list, with the numbers added in to help you keep track:

But the fruit of the Spirit is

(1) love

(2) joy

(3) peace

(4) longsuffering

(5) kindness

(6) goodness

(7) faithfulness

(8) gentleness

(9) self-control

Later I learned that Mr. Morgan had asked each of the kids in his study group to focus on just one of the nine "fruits" in the above verses. And, to be ready to explain it when they got back together on that very evening, along with supplying a Bible verse or two to back up their explanation. So once Mr. Morgan got out of the picture, what came next moved along fairly quick and smooth, without a lot of fussing around. But first, as you'll see in a moment, he had something else to say.

"The first one of the fruits the Apostle Paul talks about in these verses," Mr. Morgan began, "is 'love.' But I don't think Paul was talking about the kind of love between a man and a woman—for example, the kind of love between your own parents, although that would certainly be part of it. What do you think he meant in the bigger picture—and what could you use for an example? Jamie?"

Believe it or not, I hadn't realized that Jamie Goldstein was there that night. He'd been my best friend since we started school together, but he must have come in late because I wasn't even aware that he was sitting there quietly, halfway around the circle.

(1) "Uh . . . I think the kind of love Paul meant was the kind that goes out to practically everyone else. It's not an 'I love you with all my heart!' kind of thing so much as it's a feeling of friendship and goodwill toward other people. No hating; no making too much fun; no being mean. Just trying to see someone's best points and making a real effort to be fair—to be straight with them. Like when you say 'Nice job!' to your sister when she draws a good picture of your mother even when the first three tries are so awful she throws them away."

Mr. Morgan smiled. "Very good, Jamie! Now, did you find some Bible verses to support all that?"

Jamie looked confused for a second or so, and then he caught on and looked at some note paper he was holding. "Oh yeah! What I picked out would be Luke 6:27–28, which included something that Jesus Himself said over and over again. Here's how it goes:

> 'But I say unto you which hear, love your enemies, do good to them which hate you, bless them that curse you, and pray for them which despitefully use you.'"

Mr. Morgan nodded his head, then closed his eyes and seemed to be thinking about something else while everyone waited for him to comment on what Jamie had just read. Finally, he opened his eyes.

"Very good, Jamie," he said. "I think you've hit it right on the head. Because, the Bible tells us many times that God is love. *This is who God is!* This is also why the first fruit of the Spirit is love itself. Everything starts there. God wants us to be like Him, and the best way to be like Him is to start by loving other people. From that beginning, like when you plant something in good soil and remember to water it, the other fruits of the Spirit can then grow and develop.

"In fact"—and here Mr. Morgan seemed to hesitate for just a second before he continued—"as I look around this room I realize that we have a wonderful example of what Jesus was talking about right here. You all know what happened to Harry Page, one of the boys at school, when the baseball hit him in the face a few days ago. Right?"

When almost everyone nodded, Mr. Morgan continued.

"I had a long talk with Harry's father the

next morning, and he told me something some of you might not know. It seems that the one person who was most concerned about Harry when all this happened was the one who got to him first and held his head up so he wouldn't drown in his own blood. She then rode to the doctor's office with him and his father, and probably kept him from bleeding to death. And yet, I've been told that the young man who was injured was someone who had not been exactly nice to the young lady I'm talking about, for the last year or so. Anybody know who I mean?"

Probably half the kids in the room twisted around and looked at Cake Baker, who turned as red as a beet and lowered her head like she was hoping she could disappear.

"Now again," Mr. Morgan continued. "Let's not confuse the kind of love we're talking about here with anything romantic. But on the other hand, Jesus made it very clear that we need to work especially hard to help those who act like they 'hate' us—those who even 'curse' us and 'despitefully use' us, which is simply another way of saying those who mistreat us or make fun of us on purpose."

He paused again, then nodded toward little Miss Redface.

"Cake, what you did for Harry was probably one of the best examples I've heard about in a long time. And even though you might be a little bit embarrassed to have it pointed out, that's exactly the kind of behavior that Jesus Christ Himself was talking about in the verses Jamie just read."

After what seemed like ten minutes or so, Mr. Morgan took the pressure off Cake Baker. You could almost see her start breathing again.

"Any more questions or comments on love as the first of the nine fruits of the Spirit?" he said. When no one raised their hand he went on.

"Okay, going back to what Jamie said earlier, I want us all to remember that it always starts with love. That's exactly the way I see it, too. In fact, I want each one of you to look at all nine of these 'fruits' as a group that's arranged in a certain order in the Bible—a certain 'logical sequence,' to use some bigger words. Each fruit is one more way of living your life, of dealing with others. And each one develops within you as you walk with God and let Him teach you to be more like Him."

Mr. Morgan paused for a moment, to see if anyone had any questions. When no one did he went on to the next of the nine fruits. "Okay, who agreed to look up and learn about 'joy'?"

(2) Annie, a girl I barely knew, raised her hand. "That was mine, and I think it means being happy inside yourself, no matter what happens. You sometimes have to deal with sad things, but I think this verse is talking about a kind of joy that never really goes away, even if it sometimes seems to get covered up. Because, in your heart you always know that God loves you, that God will take care of you, and that God will be with you. You can be sad when sad things happen, but the joy in knowing God is still always there, like a rock underneath."

At that point, without even being asked, Annie instantly made the perfect biblical connection.

"In Luke 8:5–15, Jesus told a story that most of us have heard before, about a farmer who went out to sow his seed. Some fell along the path and the birds ate it. Some fell on rock, but when it tried to grow it had no water so it died. Some fell among the weeds, which grew even faster and choked it out. But some fell on good ground and grew up into a huge crop.

"Jesus taught several lessons from this story. First, the 'seed' was actually the Word of God itself. However, in verse 13 He talked about those who:

> ...*receive the word with joy; and these have no root, which for a while believe, and in time of temptation fall away.*

"In other words, even *your own joy* will wither away if it is not planted and rooted in love. At the same time, doing things for others, 'in love,' can often bring joy to them too. I think that's why I sometimes read the newspaper to my grandmother—I love to make things easier for her, and she gets joy out of not having to squint at the print so hard!"

To be honest, I was so amazed at how Annie put what she had to say that I think I almost fell over. Mr. Morgan must have felt the same way. "Annie, that was absolutely perfect!" was all he could say. And everyone around me nodded.

Then we moved on to 'peace.' "What does this one mean?" asked Mr. Morgan. "How can you have peace when half of the people in the world seem to be fighting the other half? Paisley, was that your word?"

(3) It was, and Cake was smart enough to latch on to what Annie had already said. "It's really a lot like joy," she began, "except that joy is more of a feeling that's sometimes real obvious to others, while peace is what you feel deep inside where it might not be so visible. You can see a person's joy on their face, and in the way they do things, but you can't see someone else's peace until you know them long enough to sense what they're feeling."

She stopped for a moment and I thought she was finished, but then she went on a bit more. "It's like the difference between my dog and my cat," she said. "The dog is so eager and so full of energy you can see joy written all over him whenever you come home. He just explodes and he never seems to slow down! But my cat is completely different—as calm and cool as a summer breeze, no matter what. So there's never any question that she's at peace—you couldn't be riled up inside and sleep as much as she does!"

It was hard not to laugh at that one. When things had quieted back down, Mr. Morgan spoke again. "That was outstanding,

Paisley. Maybe the perfect way to think of the difference between joy and peace. Just compare it to dogs and cats! Now, can you show us how all that connects to the Bible?"

Cake Baker nodded. "The verse I would use would be John 14:27. Jesus made it very clear that He meant for His disciples to have peace in their hearts even when things were rough in other parts of their lives. He also offered the same kind of inner peace to everyone else who accepted salvation through Him. Here's what He said about it:

> *Peace I leave with you, my peace I give unto you: not as the world giveth, give I unto you. Let not your heart be troubled, neither let it be afraid.*

"Soon after this, Jesus returned to heaven to be with His Father. And that, of course, is where we will go if we give our hearts to Him while we're here on earth! This is why He told us not to let our hearts be troubled, and not to be afraid."

"Wow! That's another one, absolutely perfect, Miss Baker," said Mr. Morgan, smiling broadly. He paused for a moment, looked around the room to see if anyone else had a question, glanced back at his list, and then continued.

"Jim—it says here that you would talk about 'longsuffering.' But first, that may be a bit of an old-fashioned term—what should that mean to us, in more familiar language?"

(4) "'Longsuffering' means 'patience,'" said Jim. "I didn't know that at first so I looked it up. It means not getting riled up if someone else doesn't do what we think they should do, as fast as we think they should do it. Like when we're waiting in line to buy something at the store and the clerk's not moving very fast.

"It also means not coming unglued when we're trying to help someone else learn something and they don't get it right away. It's about staying in the game right to the end, like a pitcher who doesn't give up when he gets three balls and no strikes on a batter."

"Excellent," said Mr. Morgan. That pitcher would also need lots of confidence in his ability, wouldn't he? Patience with others is one thing. Patience with yourself—even when you know you can do what you're being asked to do—can be something else entirely."

"Yeah—like learning all the ballet positions, and how to move with your partner without getting stepped on!" said one of the girls. Not too many of the guys really understood, but most of us tried not to groan anyway. As Annie and Cake had done, Jim then went directly into the biblical connection he'd already worked out.

"In the book of Job," he continued, "in the Old Testament, God allowed the devil to test a man named Job by sending him a big bunch of troubles. I guess the devil thought he could make Job turn away from God, for these were things that might make many people think that God hated them.

"But Job trusted God above everything else. And, God had given him a lot of patience—so much that he was able to stand up under the worst the devil could do to him. And in the end, God took wonderful care of Job.

"I want to read five or six verses to show you what happened after the devil was finally shoved out of the game. I'm taking these from the forty-second chapter of Job. Verse 10 tells us that God 'turned' the captivity of Job after he prayed for his friends. By 'turned' I believe this means that God stopped letting him be tested and turned things around, after Job prayed for the people who were giving him bad advice and were telling him to turn away from God. This is what God did for him after that, in Job 42:12–16:

> *So the LORD blessed the latter end of Job more than his beginning: for he had fourteen thousand sheep, and six thousand camels, and a thousand yoke of oxen, and a thousand she asses. He had also seven sons and three daughters. And he called the name of the first, Jemima; and the name of the second, Kezia; and the name of the third, Kerenhappuch.*
>
> *And in all the land were no women found so fair as the daughters of Job: and their father gave them inheritance among their brethren. After this lived Job an hundred and forty years, and saw his sons, and his sons' sons, even four generations.*

"Most of us will never need as much patience as Job had, but it's good to read his story to remember to *trust God even when things don't look so good!*"

"All right," Mr. Morgan went on, smiling as ever. "That was terrific! Now we're up to 'kindness.' Who has kindness?"

(5) "I did and I hope I do!" said Eric Topper, one of the guys who sat right next to me in class at school. "By which I mean that I hope I show it to others enough so you know it's real. Kindness is another of those things you can't fake. You either treat other people without being mean and snarly, or you don't. Like when you tell your aunt that her hat looks good even if the rest of her clothes are weird.

"Except for the times when you're just trying to survive without getting smacked, kindness is pretty much out there for everyone else to see. Or not to see.

"Now, I thought about this one for two or three days, trying to figure out what would be the best story from the Bible. Finally, my dad suggested that I look in one of the books in the Old Testament that tells the story of King David. And that's where I found my example, in the ninth chapter of Second Samuel.

"According to the Bible, Saul was the first king of the nation of Israel and Jonathan was his son. Jonathan was also David's best friend. When David and Jonathan were young men they spent a lot of time together. But during one of the wars between the Philistines and the Israelites, Jonathan was killed.

"A few years later, David himself became the king of Israel. One day, according to 2 Samuel 9:1, he remembered his best friend and asked his own servants:

Is there yet any that is left of the house of Saul, that I may shew him kindness for Jonathan's sake?

"When he was told that Jonathan's son, Mephibosheth (Meh-fib-oh-sheth), was still alive, David sent his servants to bring him and his family to David's house. David then gave land to him and told Mephibosheth's servants to help him farm it. He also told his own servants to seat Mephibosheth at his own table at mealtime, so that he ate his meals with David's family for the rest of his life.

"This was kindness at its best, way above the call of duty and honor."

Mr. Morgan waited a moment or two before he responded. "Thank you, Eric," he finally said. "That's an amazing story. Does anyone have any questions? Anything to add?"

Nobody did, so he went on. "Next up is 'goodness.' Who has goodness?"

(6) This time Cake's hand shot up again. "We didn't have enough people last week so I took two of them," she said. "I think 'goodness' as it's used here in the Bible is the partner to the one that went before, kindness. I think it's like I said about joy and peace—the first is out in the open where others can see it; the second is inside where it's not so visible. So kindness is what you show to others, based on the goodness you have inside."

She waited a few seconds, to see if anyone had any questions, then went on. "Now, as far as a biblical example is concerned, I found what I was looking for in Mark 12:41–44. This passage tells about a woman who put all the money she had into the offering box in the temple, for helping other people. She threw in 'two mites,' which would be a very tiny amount in modern money. I guess maybe a penny or two—but it was all she had.

"Here's what Jesus said about her in verses 43 and 44:

And he called unto him his disciples, and saith unto them, Verily I say unto you, That this poor widow hath cast more in, than all they which have cast into the treasury: For all they did cast in of their abundance; but she of her want did cast in all that she had, even all her living.

"This woman put her money in the box to do good for other people. And I think that doing good things simply because you want to is the best possible example of how goodness should work in the real world."

By the time Cake finished talking people were nodding all over the room, Mr. Morgan included. "Not much I can add to that," he finally said. "Who's next, with 'faithfulness'?"

(7) The girl who had that one—I didn't know her name—spoke in such a monotone it was hard to hear what she was saying, but I managed to figure it out. "I think it means being faithful to other people—not giving

up on them, not double-crossing them, not running away when they're in trouble," she said. "It's like how your mother takes extra care of you when you feel sick, even though it might be a lot easier to close the door and leave you alone."

"That's good," said Mr. Morgan. "Anything else? Anyone other than ourselves and our friends we should be faithful to?"

My hand went up and I found myself talking, with Mr. Morgan's permission, almost in spite of my original intent to keep my mouth shut. "I think faithfulness to God also plays a big part in all this. You can't be faithful to others if you're unfaithful to Him, because that's where it starts."

To this day I still don't know where that came from. It just seemed right, and I think I surprised not only myself but Cake Baker and a few others as well.

Mr. Morgan couldn't seem to stop nodding. "Yes—yes—that's exactly right! What was your name again—Delbert? Dellie? Either way, I think you made a terrific point. So often we talk about faithfulness as though it's only a measure of how faithful we are to our friends and our family, or how faithful they are to us. But it starts with God—He's faithful to us no matter what, and we can learn to be faithful—to Him and to others—by following His example."

For a moment I thought Cake Baker would bust out crying, she looked so proud and happy to have me there. The only problem for me is that I still can't explain where I got what I said. And yet, the minute it came out of my mouth I knew it was true. Plus, a lot of stuff that happened to me later on, long after I got older and learned what it meant to have faithful friends, seemed to just "come" to me in the same way. On the other hand, "grew up" is not really a good term to use with me since I never got much bigger. But I definitely got older.

Finally, the girl who'd introduced this subject spoke up in a much stronger voice, using a story from the very beginning of the Bible.

"I think that what Dellie said is also what I meant to say. Because, I want to take my example from chapters 6, 7, and 8 from Genesis, and those are all about Noah. He was more faithful to God than anyone else on the earth at that time. All the others had turned their backs on God and were so wicked that, in order to keep the human race from becoming totally sinful, God had to destroy all the evil people and start over with Noah. So God told Noah to build a boat big enough to hold his whole family, plus two each of all the animals on earth.

"I think you all know the rest of the story—how the rains came, how Noah and his family floated in the ark, how it settled onto the top of a mountain, and how the rains and the floods finally stopped and the land dried out again.

"But that's not the main point here. What really matters is how faithful to God Noah was. God told him what to do and Noah did it, even though—with his own eyes—he could see no need to build such a huge boat. Yet he believed God and stayed faithful to Him. You can be sure that many of his neighbors laughed at him and called him a fool, but Noah's faithfulness paid off in a big way.

"In the end, when Noah and his family came out of the ark onto dry land, Noah built an altar and worshipped God. In Genesis

8:21–22, God then said:

> *...and the LORD said in his heart, I will not again curse the ground any more for man's sake; for the imagination of man's heart is evil from his youth; neither will I again smite any more every thing living, as I have done. While the earth remaineth, seedtime and harvest, and cold and heat, and summer and winter, and day and night shall not cease.*

"I would say that Noah did all of us a huge favor, by showing God that at least one human being—plus his family—could make it worthwhile for God to give us all a second chance simply by being faithful to Him."

At that point we had just two more fruits to go—"gentleness" and "self-control." The girl who dealt with gentleness covered the subject in a very quick, clear summary.

(8) "When I think of gentleness I think of how I would hold a baby chick. Or how I might pick up a caterpillar if I didn't want to hurt it.

"Except that gentleness is more about how we treat other people. It's a part of faithfulness, kindness, goodness, and the others. If we're kind to others we'll be gentle, too. If we're good to others we'll be gentle as well. And if we're patient with others we'll be gentle to them every bit as much.

"Jesus Christ Himself was by far the best example of gentleness in the whole Bible. He even said so Himself in Matthew 11:29:

Take my yoke upon you and learn of me, for I am meek and lowly in heart: and ye shall find rest unto your souls.

"And yet, Jesus never backed away from the truth. He always told it like it was, but He was never mean or too rough. For example, He told many people how to be saved but always in a gentle way with a gentle voice.

"One of the few times Jesus spoke in a non-gentle way happened when he drove the money changers out of the temple. But they were doing evil things in God's own house so He had a right to be angry. In fact, He had a duty to do what He did.

"This proves that Jesus was not afraid to be strong when He needed to be. The trick is in knowing when, so you can be gentle and kind at all other times. Also, some people say that being tough at the right time is really the kindest thing you can do in the long run, but that's another huge subject!"

Mr. Morgan smiled and nodded, and since no one else could add anything we moved on to the last of the "fruits."

"Who has 'self-control'?" said Mr. Morgan.

"I sure hope I do," said Joey Falcon. "I need it most every day!" As with so many others in the room, Joey had done his homework and had it nailed.

(9) "Self-control is also like so many of the other fruits," he went on. "It means that you don't always slug somebody in the shoulder when they bump into you. You also don't do some of the mean and spiteful things—like telling lies or swiping their books—that come so naturally when someone else bugs you.

"'Naturally,' that is, if you don't have God in you. But if you do have His Spirit inside you, you learn to stop and think about everything you're about to say or do. You want to make sure it's the right way to show other people who you really are—how you really feel inside, with God in there too."

He himself stopped to think for a moment, and Mr. Morgan almost jumped in, but Joey wasn't quite finished yet even before he opened up his Bible.

"God is not about smashing around like a wild bull that's had a rope thrown around his neck but won't give up until he breaks a few arms and legs. He's more like a trained racehorse that runs full speed only when the time is right. Along with all that horse's other training, he's learned self-control. Anything else is wild and crazy—you can't be self-controlled and out-of-control at the same time.

"I think that the story of Daniel gives us a great lesson in the value of self-control. In the first chapter of the book of Daniel, he and three of his friends were taken by King Nebuchadnezzar (Neb-uh-kud-nez-zar) to Babylon and ordered to serve the king. They were also expected to eat rich foods and drink wines from the king's table. But Daniel and his friends had enough self-control to resist eating what they knew would not be good for them, especially since they were still young and hadn't finished growing up.

"Here's what Daniel said to the people in charge, in Daniel 1:12–13:

Prove thy servants, I beseech thee, ten days; and let them give us pulse (vegetables) to eat, and water to drink. Then let our countenances be looked upon before thee, and the countenance of the children that eat of the portion of the king's meat: and as thou seest, deal with thy servants.

"You probably know how this story ended, too! After the ten days had passed, Daniel and his friends felt better and looked healthier than all the other young men who were eating rich foods and drinking wine. But only because those four young men all had self-control."

By the time Joey finally finished, Mr. Morgan had almost lost his own self-control. "Wow," he said, his head bobbing up and down and his smile spread out about as wide as any I'd ever seen. "You folks have really got it! You've really got it! And the best thing about all this is the way you've tied these things together. Because"—and here he paused for several seconds, with his finger in the air—"because you've caught on to one of the biggest pieces of truth in the whole Bible, and you've come back to it over and over.

"These 'fruits' that the Apostle Paul talks about are not natural to any of us without God's Spirit living inside us. At the same time, they don't all explode out of us like pieces of dynamite that are set off instantly when we ask God to come in. They grow and develop from one another, which means that you start with one and that leads into the next one, and that leads into the next one. Until you're like the tree in the orchard that starts with one little bud, then a few little blossoms, and then a whole huge offering of fruits that are as perfectly developed, as ripe, and as ready to be enjoyed as they can possibly be.

"The fruits of the Spirit develop in a logical order, budding out with love and blossoming through all the others until, by the time you've been at it for a while, things like faithfulness, gentleness, and self-control can seem almost automatic. Not quite, of course—very few good things are 'automatic' in us unless we work on them. But it feels easier and easier, and more and more natural as we move ahead."

He paused and waited a moment. "Any questions on all this?"

Not a single hand went up. I had the feeling that everyone in the room had lots to think about. "Perfect," said Mr. Morgan. Let me close with a prayer and let's wrap it up for tonight. No homework for next week—we'll do a little review and then start on a whole new subject."

Cake and I both ate two or three cookies apiece before we walked back home that night, but I had so much to think about I still wasn't very hungry.

BUILDING ON A FOUNDATION

CHAPTER 6

A day or two later, Cake and I were both out in our front yards at the same time. I wandered across the street to look at an old, rain-soaked baseball glove she pulled out from under one of the bushes lining her front porch, and we wound up talking.

"So Dellie—I don't want to pry, but what did you think about the other night?"

"What do you mean?"

"Well, I just wondered if you had any questions. Remember, you're the one who started all this by asking me why I was willing to help Harry Page. Did anything make sense? Did you understand that 'loving someone' doesn't have to mean anything romantic? It just means caring about other people and helping them when you can—especially if they really need it."

"Oh sure—I'd heard some of that before. That wasn't the first time I ever came across the word 'Bible,' or 'fruits of the Spirit,' you know!"

"I do know, Dellie, but that's not the point. I don't think I've heard it all pulled together quite as well before, even by a real preacher in a real church."

"Yeah—well, sometimes big things are easier to understand when they're talked about in smaller words." I then turned to head back home, when suddenly, something made me spin around and stand there for about fifteen seconds before I spoke again.

"Cake, there is one thing I'm not sure I understand," I finally blurted out. "This whole 'fruits of the Spirit' thing makes sense only if you know what everyone means by 'having the Spirit inside of you' in the first place. I mean, you can't get something from nothing."

She knew instantly what I was trying to say. "That's a good point, Dellie, and it deserves a good answer. Do you want to go talk to Mr. Morgan? I think he's probably home for lunch right now."

"No—if you can't explain it I don't think I want to know," I said, turning back toward my own house.

"Wait! I didn't say I couldn't explain! Give me a chance!"

Cake looked more than a little panicked when I turned back to face her. But she calmed down right away and stood there very quiet for about as long as I had. Probably thinking, like I'd been doing. Finally she began to talk again, but in a much slower voice than usual.

"Dellie, it's the most simple concept in the whole Bible—even more basic than the things we talked about the other night. It's like the bricks and the concrete that go in the ground to hold up your house. You can't build on top of plain old dirt—you've got to start with something a lot more solid."

She hesitated for a moment, then continued. "Think of it another way. Do you know what the word 'comprehensive' means? Com-pre-hen-sive? That's what we're talking about here—it's a complete change in who you are. It starts out small and winds up big. Nothing is left out. Does that make any sense?"

As it happened, I already knew that word and I told her so.

"All right, then. The comprehensive change I'm talking about starts with just one thing. We are not perfect—none of us is perfect no matter how hard we might try. By ourselves we cannot be anything more than ordinary people, full of bad thoughts and bad words waiting to come out, which we can sometimes push down out of sight. But they don't stay there—they always get loose at some point and they make us far, far less than what we could be if we had the right kind of help.

"That help, as I'm sure you've heard other people say before, can only come from God. The Bible talks about it over and over, but lots of people still don't get it. If I can use another big word that you're probably familiar with, you have to 'acknowledge' that there's a big difference between you and me and the God who created us.

"That difference is called 'sin.' But here's what you have to remember. The word *sin*, by itself, doesn't have to mean terrible things like killing and robbing. Going back to what I just said, on the most simple level, sin is nothing more than the difference between God and us.

"Because," and here Cake paused for an even longer time, looking into my eyes like she was not going on until she saw whatever she was searching for. Finally I guess she found it. "Because, God Himself *is* perfect and we are not. God Himself *is* love and we are not. God Himself *is* joy, peace, kindness, goodness, and all those other things and we are not. And that's why we need His spirit to live inside us—not so He can make us perfect because that'll never happen, but so He can help us get closer and closer to Him the more we listen and respond. And eventually, so He can bring us into heaven to be with Him forever after we die."

Wow! I'd never heard it laid out quite that way before, even though I'd already been to church a fair number of times at that point in my life. I didn't know what to say, and so I said nothing for at least a whole minute. Finally, Cake added one more thought.

"The thing is," she said, "any of us can have God's Spirit inside anytime we want. All we have to do is ask Him for it, without trying to pretend anything at all. The fact is, you can't pretend; it has to be real on your part before He can make it real on His part. There just isn't any other way, and yet it's the simplest thing in the world to do once you agree in your heart to reach out to Him. Just ask Him. Just tell Him you're ready and ask Him to come in."

By that time Cake was almost whispering. In a way, somewhere in the back of my mind I realized that talking quietly made me want what she was talking about a hundred times more than if she'd been yelling at me. But I still wasn't ready.

"I don't know, Cake," I finally said. "You make it sound good but I'm not sure. I need a chance to think. Can we talk about this again in a few days?"

"Of course. Whenever you're ready. I can help you; Mr. Morgan can help you. But in the end you really don't need either one of us. It's between you and God, and only God can speak for Himself."

That ended our conversation but the subject did not go away.

THE GIRL IN THE RIVER

CHAPTER 7

A day or two later I still was not quite sure how to figure all this out, so I went fishing. Normally I would have gone with Jamie Goldstein or some of the other guys, but Jamie was working for his dad on that particular day and I really didn't think I wanted to talk to anyone else. Not even Cake Baker—she was the one who'd started so many of these new thoughts swirling around in my head in the first place.

There was a great spot along the main river that ran through town, not more than eight or ten blocks from my house, where the ground was grassy and smooth. We could throw in a line, prop up our poles on rocks with the thick ends stuck in little holes we'd gouge out of the ground, and wait for something to bite. A nice big perch or a bass if we were lucky. That left a lot of time for talking and fussing around with the guys. Or, for thinking about whatever was on your mind if you were alone.

It took me a little while to dig up some bait and get my pole together. The last time out I'd broken part of the top off my bobber—the little painted cork gizmo with the wooden rod sticking up that bobbed up and down to warn you when a fish was nibbling at your bait. I'd glued it back together the day before, but I had to take off the string that was holding the top piece on—and make sure the glue was completely dry—before I dared to throw it in the water again.

It was probably two o'clock in the afternoon before I got to our usual place and settled down. The sun had been fairly warm until an hour or two earlier, but then the wind had come up. I figured we might get some rain before the day was gone, but I didn't really care. The other guys and I weren't entirely stupid—the spot we'd picked out had lots of late afternoon shade from two big trees that stood right on the bank. At that time of the year their leaves were also thick enough to keep us fairly dry if we stayed close to the trunks when it rained.

And yes, I know you're not supposed to hide under a tree in a storm. But the thing is, we knew we could always run across the road and get under a roof that had a huge metal lightning rod on top if the lightning ever got too fierce. Because, beyond our two trees was an unpaved road and straight across the road was a blacksmith shop, attached to a livery stable where they kept the doors open all day during the summer, to let the fresh air in. It was run by one of my dad's friends, a guy named Judd Mason. He took care of the small carriage my family owned, along with shoeing our horse and checking him out whenever he seemed a little less ready-to-go than usual.

The ground itself, sloping down from the trees toward the river, was smooth and completely covered with grass for ten or fifteen feet. Then it turned into dirt and dropped almost straight down for about six feet to the surface of the water. As a younger kid I'd been warned many times to stay away from the edge, until I finally learned to swim. Or, at least, that's what I called it—I could paddle myself down to the bottom and up to the surface, but I wasn't exactly an expert at any of the basic strokes.

Even so, to get back on land I then had to go about twenty feet to the right, along the bank to the point where it sloped down to be almost level with the edge of the water itself. That was the beginning of our local beach, which is where we went swimming when we were in the mood.

Unlike the place where we threw in our fishing lines, our swimming spot was also fairly shallow, although I had trouble standing up if I went more than a dozen feet from the shore. But I didn't care. Given my size I knew I'd never be a world-class speed swimmer no matter how hard I tried. But I could navigate and that was enough for me.

Most of the time, if no one was splashing around too close to it, the water in our fishing hole was pretty clear. In fact, even though the river was a good twenty-five or thirty feet deep in that one spot—and maybe eighty to a hundred feet wide—if the water wasn't stirred up you could sometimes see all the way to the bottom. On the other hand, if the wind was blowing as hard as it was that afternoon it could make ripples on the top, big and cresty enough—like little waves—to make the whole thing look about as clear as a bowl of gravy.

On that afternoon I'd probably sat there, watching my bobber, for a good hour or so.

But in truth I wasn't really paying much attention to it. As it had been for two or three days by then, my mind was still on what I'd heard during the youth meeting at Mr. Morgan's house. For the first time in my life I felt that maybe I was beginning to understand something that had always been like a mystery to me before that evening.

The whole idea—that God doesn't insist that we be "perfect" the instant we give our hearts to Him—seemed a lot more fair than what I thought I'd heard from others before. God *should* be eager to help us become more like Him. But, the only way He can do that almost has to be one little step at a time. And even then we can never be perfect, like He is. But we can become a lot better than we could ever be on our own, especially in the way we treat each other.

The word *love* kept coming back to my mind. I almost felt like someone was asking me, "How much do you love others, Dellie? How much do you care how things work out for other people? How much are you willing to help someone you don't even know—or someone who's never been very nice to you, like Cake Baker helped Harry Page?"

And then it happened. Even as I sat there with my mind completely occupied I heard something going on across the road and turned around to see what it was. A two-horse carriage had just pulled up, outside the livery stable. As soon as it stopped, a woman I'd never seen before climbed down from the front and went inside. Then, a minute or so later Judd Mason came out to unhitch the horses and move them into the stable area. He then came back out, lifted up one of the long wooden bars on the front that would normally be fastened to the horse, and fussed with the part that hooked onto the carriage until he got it completely off.

At that point he laid it on the ground and went to work on the other one. I figured he must have intended to replace them both, or do some kind of work on each one. Once they were off he picked them both up together, carried them into his shop, and then walked back outside, around the main building, until he moved out of sight behind it. In a few seconds I heard another door slam . . . and that's when it happened.

Exactly what the "it" was I couldn't say, because I had turned back to my bobber by then. I figured that everything interesting had already occurred. But there was a definite slope leading from the stable doors and across the road to the riverbank. Somehow, I think the woman who'd been driving the carriage—something pretty unusual for that era, by the way—had not locked the brake. Or, Mr. Judd forgot to brace the carriage wheels before he went behind the building. Either way, once the two hitching bars were no longer there to drag on the ground there was nothing to stop the carriage from rolling backwards. Or to even slow it down. A strong gust of wind might have been all it took to get it started.

A few seconds later I heard someone scream and I spun around again, but by that time the carriage had picked up speed and was already halfway across the road. And it seemed to be moving faster with every fraction of a second.

"No! Stop it! Stop it! My baby's inside! I left my little girl inside!"

The same woman who'd driven up a few minutes earlier came running toward me from across the road, skirts pulled up and hair flying in the wind. I almost can't describe what her face looked like, except to say that it was as close to pure terror as anything I'd ever seen.

Before I could even move, the carriage rattled down the last fifteen feet and looped out beyond the edge of the bank, into the river. It made a huge splash, gurgled for a few seconds, and sank below the surface faster than I could even take it all in.

"No!" she screamed again. "No! My baby! My baby! She was asleep on the seat! My little girl is still inside!"

Later on that same day I learned that the lady's husband—with the help of some other guys—had loaded the baggage area with two big anvils, wrapped in wooden boxes, which he was sending over to the livery stable. Judd Mason had gone to the building behind his stables to get some help unloading them because they were too heavy for one person. That's almost for sure why the carriage itself sank so quickly.

But I didn't know that then. In truth I don't think I knew anything at all at that moment. My mind was completely blank except for one terrible thought. I had to do something or that baby would drown. I couldn't let that happen! So I threw off my shoes and jumped in the water.

I don't know how many seconds it took me to get down to the bottom. I could see the outline of the carriage, but even though the water should have been clear that far below the surface, the carriage itself had stirred up a lot of mud when it landed. Yet in spite of all that, I saw in a flash that I could never open it up from either side. Somehow, the carriage had rolled another three or four feet after it hit the bottom, straight into a lockup between two huge stones that blocked both of the doors.

"Oh dear God! Please help me! Please help me! You know I can't do this alone!"

At that exact moment my eyes fell on a big stone about the size of a softball, lying on the riverbed just five or six feet away. To be honest I'm not sure how I saw it, because the water wasn't exactly clear at that point, either. But when I pulled it out of the mud it had a smooth part sticking out on one side, just big enough for me to grab onto. Almost like a handle that someone had put there on purpose.

I knew instantly what I had to do. The

carriage had a small back window, and I remember hoping with all my heart that the opening would be big enough for me to get through if I could somehow get the glass out of the way. And I had to do it fast once I started, because I also knew that if the inside wasn't already full of water it would fill up mighty fast once I opened up a brand-new hole.

I held the rock with one hand, fumbled my way back to the carriage, and wrapped both hands around the smooth part of the rock as tight as I could. *Wham!* I smashed the rock against the glass . . . but nothing happened. *Wham! Wham! Wham!* Three times more, and then suddenly, on the fourth or fifth smack I saw a small crack start to spread across the glass.

Wham! Wham! Wham! Now I had a huge piece knocked out and the water really began pouring past me, into the carriage. For the next few seconds all I could do was feel with my hands, and pound with my rock, until I couldn't find any more sharp, pointed edges sticking out.

Even so, I felt the leftover glass scraping my back as I forced my way in, grabbing at the inside wall above my head and pulling with my arms until I got my shoulders through. But where was the baby? The water was still coming in so fast I couldn't see a thing.

Suddenly, in the muck and the murk I saw something move. I don't know how I ever got over to it—at that point I think I was pushing myself with my feet against the inside wall, but I can't be sure. And besides, it really doesn't matter because what I'd seen was definitely a very small person. I knew that instantly when my hands touched her. She was floating inside a blanket, still on the surface of the water and maybe an inch or so below the roof of the carriage. But I knew the blanket would get waterlogged and help drag her down at any second.

I don't have any idea how much time it took me to fumble my way back to the broken window. I had to hold the baby outside the carriage while I worked my way back out, and once or twice I thought I was stuck for sure. But somehow I made it, and then I was paddling as hard as I could with one hand, holding the baby tight against my body with the other, fighting to get back to the surface.

When my head cleared the water I saw

Judd Mason, running down the slope toward the woman on the edge, who was still standing there screaming. The minute he saw me he jumped in, and a few seconds later he was right there beside me. Together we thrashed our way downriver to where the bank was only a foot or so above the water. He hauled himself out first, then took the baby in one hand and pulled me out with the other.

The baby's mother was there, beside me and Judd, by the time I got back on land.

THE PERFECT FIT

CHAPTER 8

The baby herself looked pretty blue and wrinkled, and I wasn't too sure she was breathing. But her mother grabbed her, turned her upside down, and smacked her bottom just like she was a newborn.

In response the baby gasped out loud and spit up an ounce or two of dirty-looking water. Her mother immediately turned her right side up again and blew some air into her mouth—but very gently, like she was drying off a butterfly's wings. Almost immediately the baby started to cry, while her mother shucked off her wet clothes and wrapped her up in her own big scarf. Then she started to cry, too.

"Oh—thank you! Thank you! She's alive! She's alive!" That's just about all she could say while she cuddled the baby close to her face and kept her warm. After a minute or two of that we all walked back to Judd Mason's house, behind the livery stable. Judd's wife found a fresh blanket for the baby, whose name I learned was Hannah Bandela. Her mother didn't seem to realize that the kids would change that to either "Hannah Banana" or "Hannah Bandana" in a few more years, but at the time I didn't think I should bring it up.

Mrs. Mason also tried to find something dry for me to wear, too, but she didn't have any kids and all she could come up with was a flannel shirt eleven sizes too big, plus a pair of pants so long I almost couldn't roll the bottoms up far enough to take a step. But I didn't care—by then I was really cold, so I much preferred to wrap myself up in another blanket, right over the top of those clothes, until I warmed up again.

Judd himself disappeared into a bedroom and came back out a few minutes later, his wet hair combed and dry clothes on. They already had a small fire going in the fireplace, so he threw on more wood and we all sat around it for an hour or so, warming up and calming down.

Finally, Mr. Judd went outside, hitched up some horses, and offered to take us all home. On the way, Mrs. Bandela showed me

Hannah's pink little face, by then so peaceful and calm and perfectly healthy. "She owes her life to you," her mother said, "and I'll make sure she never forgets."

"That's all right," I said. "I'm just glad I was able to help. It was a scary time but I'm glad it all worked out."

"The strange thing," she went on, "is that—based on how this all happened—I don't think there's another person in town who'd be strong and mature enough to do what you did, yet small enough to fit through that opening in the back of the carriage. And do it all so fast! You were a godsend, Dellie. A true godsend, sent straight down here at exactly the right moment. I won't forget that, either!"

By that time we were approaching my neighborhood and I was only too happy to get inside, where my mother could put some ointment on my sore back. Turns out I had some real scrapes back there, not bad enough to bleed me dry but painful enough to hurt for three or four more days.

Mrs. Bandela insisted on coming in with me, to talk to my parents. By then it was very late in the afternoon, so I was grateful to have someone else explain why I'd been gone so long.

On the following morning Mrs. Bandela must have talked to someone in the local newspaper office, too, because in the afternoon they sent a reporter over to talk to me and get my side of the story. The day after that was Thursday and they ran a front-page article in the morning paper, calling me a hero. Strangely enough, a year or so after that, when they thought I'd tripped up the world's clumsiest bank robber, the local newspaper sent out the same guy to talk to me again and printed the same kind of article. But that's another story entirely.

Thursday afternoon, some Good Samaritan even found my fishing pole and brought it by my house, which seemed awfully kind at the time. A bit later on, Cake Baker knocked on the door and asked me if I'd go to the meeting of her youth group with her again that evening. For me it was a no-brainer, and Cake and I wound up talking for a couple of hours—so long, in fact, that my mother invited her to stay for supper.

That evening, when Cake and I walked into Brian Morgan's house, at least a dozen people were already there. They instantly stood up and started clapping and cheering. At first I was confused, but once I realized it was all for me I wished I hadn't come!

I'm sure I smiled and thanked everyone, but to be honest the whole evening was a blur, except for the moment when Mr. Morgan asked me to put aside all the talk about glory and honor and tell them how I really felt about what had happened two days before. I think he knew exactly what he was doing, because that broke the dam. Finally, I got my eyes dried enough to see, and recovered my voice enough to talk without choking on every word.

"I'm sorry, but I don't believe in God anymore," I finally said—in the shakiest voice I'd ever heard come out of my own mouth. "I don't believe in Him, because after what happened two days ago I know for sure that He's not only real but He cares about me, of all people. And He cares about that little baby, and He cares about her mother, too. I don't just believe anymore because I absolutely know!"

At that point my eyes filled up again and it took me at least a whole minute to get my voice back. Finally, I started once more.

"Plus, He knows exactly how to work things out when the time comes, because there's just no way any of this could have happened quickly enough to save that baby's life. He kept enough water out, all by Himself, so little Hannah could breathe a few times before the window broke. And then He got us out of there and back to the top of the river before either one of us ran out of breath or took in too much water."

I don't think anyone else said a word for another whole minute, but I wasn't the only one with watered-up eyes in that room. Mrs. Morgan finally put her arms around me and hugged me, and that broke the dam one more time.

"You realize, Dellie, that only God could have known that you'd be the perfect fit."

For a minute I didn't understand, but she gave me a few seconds to catch on before she continued. "How long do you think you were underwater yourself?"

I didn't have a clue so I could only shake my head. "I've thought about that ever since it happened and I still don't really know. But I think it must have been at least two minutes, in ice-cold water, on a single breath. And you know my lungs can't possibly be that big."

I didn't have to explain a thing beyond that. Everyone knew exactly what I was talking about.

The only other thing I remember about that evening came when Mr. Morgan insisted on talking, once again, about fruits of the Spirit. "I think the process has already started for you, Dellie," he began. "No matter how much God got involved, you couldn't possibly have cared enough to risk your life that way without feeling some kind of love for that little person. You were also faithful, patient, and unbelievably self-controlled at the same time. And now I'm sure you feel joy and peace about the whole thing, all of which are 'fruits' that come directly from God Himself."

I didn't know how to answer so I just sat there. But I knew Mr. Morgan was right, because the same thoughts had worked their way through my head a dozen times over the last two days.

Later that evening, Cake Baker and I walked home together again. I think we held hands part of the way, not because there was anything else going on but simply because we felt such a bond. A God-bond, if you know what I mean. We were two of His beloved children, and both of us knew it for sure. That's part of what I think we'll all be so aware of when we're in heaven together, someday.

When we got to my place, Cake Baker planted a smacker on my cheek before she let me go in. Many years later I'm still trying to figure out how I feel about that.

FINAL THOUGHTS

CHAPTER 9

Lots of other things happened to Cake Baker and me over the next few years. In a funny kind of way I think that some of our friends in school expected us to "get romantic" someday and marry each other, but it didn't work out that way.

By the time she graduated from high school Cake had fallen off the ladder for Harry Page, the same guy who gave her such a hard time when we were younger. Once he got his face back together he grew up strong and turned out to be a lot more athletic than I could ever be. He wound up playing baseball for one of the few minor league teams that were around in those days, and Cake was happy to teach Sunday school and do some coaching with the younger athletes in their church, including their own kids.

And somewhere along the line I guess Harry stopped making nasty remarks.

I got older but not much bigger, as I think

I've said already. I moved to Missouri when I was about twenty, where I became a singer and a dancer on the ragtime circuit. Ragtime was a special kind of American music, mostly for piano, which came along before jazz. And the "ragtime circuit" was a string of cities and towns where the main performers played for big crowds and got lots of applause.

All of that is what came along before vaudeville, which was then pushed out of the way by television. And if any of those words don't mean much to you, you'll have to look them up for yourself! The only other thing I might mention is that I knew a lot of the ragtime greats—Tom Turpin, James Scott, Scott Joplin, and a few others as well.

Along the way I met a beautiful girl named Lorelei, who was a better match for me than anyone else I could ever imagine. But it didn't start out that way—we had some scary times before things turned in our favor. Maybe nothing quite as scary as the baby-in-the-river adventure, but who's counting?

Beyond all that I'm not going to say much more, except for this. Somewhere along the line I picked up an old saying that was probably ancient even before I ever heard it: "If ya wanna know ya gotta go." That might sound a little obvious but it's actually quite true. Just like me, you'll run into lots of things in life that you won't understand if you don't get involved.

I'd heard of the fruits of the Spirit before going to that meeting with Cake Baker at the Morgans' house, but I had no idea how they might work before that night. And I'm not saying that by the time I rescued that little baby—who started making what we called "talkies" in the 1920s and then became a movie star, by the way!—I was showing "love" all over the place, either.

To use one more big word, it's a "progressive" thing before it becomes what Cake called "comprehensive." In other words, God doesn't turn you into a better person all at once. That would be like pouring paint from an airplane onto your house and expecting to get a perfect result. Just like you don't become a world-class figure skater, carpenter, singer, or fireman in one day. He helps you build yourself up a little at a time. So, in the end the change is real and it doesn't ever have to go away.

At the same time, my friend Jamie Goldstein told me something about his family one day that really made sense. At that time his mother already had eight kids, and she often told them she didn't expect any of them to be perfect all the time. But, that together they should be able to keep the house in shape and keep everyone fed whenever she had to take a day or two off to have another baby. Each one could do something, no matter how small.

That's a good way to look at what people often call "fellowship" in a church, or in a small, in-home group like the one Cake Baker took me to. Each of us helps the other.

Okay—that's enough for now. Just remember that I'm pretty old, looking back over many, many years when I tell you these things. I was never perfect, and I seemed to forget about God more than once, but only for short periods of time here and there. Because He never forgot about me. He knew my name from the day I was born. He also knew all the knife throwers, kidnappers, riverboat workers, and physical giants I had to deal with along the way.

He knows your name, too.

APPENDIX 1

Something to Think About

1) Dellie O'Shea took a whole bunch of space to tell you about himself before the story started. Why was that important in helping you understand what happened later on?

_____

_____

_____

_____

_____

_____

_____

2) What was your immediate reaction to the way Cake Baker helped Harry Page when he got hurt? Were you surprised? Did you wonder why, when he'd been so mean to her before?

_____

_____

_____

_____

3) Put yourself in Cake Baker's place. Why do you think she didn't want to try to explain to Dellie, all by herself, why she helped Harry Page?

_____
_____
_____
_____
_____
_____
_____
_____

4) Had you heard of the fruits of the Spirit before you read this story? If so, what was your understanding?

_____
_____
_____
_____
_____
_____
_____
_____

5) What did it mean to you when Mr. Morgan explained that all the fruits of the

Spirit "start with love"? Why would that be true—can't you show joy, and patience, and kindness without basing them on love?

_____

_____

_____

_____

_____

_____

_____

6) Of all the fruits of the Spirit, which ones do you feel like you have in your own heart already? Can you give some examples of how you have shown them to others in the past?

_____

_____

_____

_____

_____

_____

_____

7) Which fruit of the Spirit is hardest for you to show in your own life? Why would this be true? Do you think God can help you? How would you ask Him to do that?

_____
_____
_____
_____
_____
_____
_____
_____

8) Were there any fruits of the Spirit that didn't make sense to you? If so, which ones— and why do you think that might be true?

_____
_____
_____
_____
_____
_____
_____

9) In chapter 6 of this story, when Cake Baker talks to Dellie about "building on a foundation," what is your understanding of what that foundation should be? Have you built on it in your own life?

_____

_____

_____

_____

_____

_____

_____

_____

10) When Dellie went fishing by himself, was fishing just an excuse? If so, for what? Why would he want to go off alone?

_____

_____

_____

_____

_____

_____

_____

11) How many things can you name that had to "line up" perfectly for the little girl in the carriage to be rescued? Do you think that God could bring them all together at once, or did they all happen by chance?

_____

_____

_____

_____

_____

_____

_____

_____

12) What were Mr. Morgan's final thoughts on the condition of Dellie O'Shea's heart at the end of the story? Did Dellie agree? How did Dellie say it himself?

_____

_____

_____

_____

_____

_____

_____

APPENDIX 2

The Fruits of the Spirit in Your Own Life

Love

◆ Let your parents and your brothers and sisters know that you care for them.

◆ Treat older people with respect and affection.

◆ Take good care of your dog, your cat, and any other pets in your family.

Joy

◆ Try to see the most positive parts of everything. Focus on the good, not the bad.

◆ When you enjoy something, let other people know!

◆ Try to make things fun for other people.

Peace

◆ Try to base your life on your trust in God, not on your emotions.

◆ Try not to distract others when they need to be calm.

◆ Do not get angry when you don't get your way.

Longsuffering (Patience)
◆ Wait for your turn when playing games or answering questions in school.
◆ Let other people finish speaking before you jump in.
◆ Give others the first choice when treats are handed out. And yes, this can be a hard one but it's worth learning to do!

Kindness
◆ Don't hesitate to share things with family and friends—at home, at church, and at school.
◆ Be especially quiet and helpful whenever anyone around you is ill.
◆ Be generous in any other ways you can think of—on purpose!

Goodness
◆ Volunteer to help older members of your family—in the yard or garden, in the kitchen, or even by reading to them. Especially reading for others —older people really like that!
◆ Play with the kids at school who might not have many other friends.
◆ Help your younger brothers and sisters with their homework.

Faithfulness

◆ Spend your own private time with God each day.

◆ Pray as God has taught you, with respect and reverence. And always start by blessing Him.

◆ Build on your relationship with God by being loyal to your friends and family, as He would do.

Gentleness

◆ If you ever have to correct someone else— or bring them bad news—do so as carefully and quietly as possible.

◆ Always play with younger brothers and sisters—and friends—without being too rough or loud.

◆ Be careful with your pets and all other animals. Do not harm or distress them on purpose.

Self-Control

◆ Eat your meals quietly, without extra noise or disturbances.

◆ Complete your homework each night without complaining.

◆ Go to bed at the proper time without being grouchy or grumpy.

APPENDIX 3

Researching the Bible Online

One of the joys of the Internet is that there's almost no limit on the good things you can find if you know where to look. For people wanting to look up Bible verses, to search for particular words or concepts, or simply to read from the Bible itself, this is especially true.

For students, writers, and editors who want to quote from the Bible but don't want to key in the words on their own—especially to avoid keystroke errors in long passages—one of the more commonly used sites is called *Bible Gateway* (www.biblegateway.com). If your language is English you can look something up in more than twenty different English translations of the Bible. If your language is Spanish you have at least seven translations to choose from. Plus, you can find translations in more than twenty other languages, including Swedish, Danish, Portuguese, Vietnamese, Chinese, Korean, and several Arabic languages. You can also put various translations side by side on the screen to compare different versions.

Blue Letter Bible (www.blueletterbible.org) is another popular website. This one contains many of the Bible Gateway features but also adds commentaries, devotionals, and other tools and attractions.

In fact, so many Bible "helps" are now available online that it's almost impossible to list them all. What we recommend, instead, is Googling the words "Bible Research Online." Google will then bring up a long list of terrific possibilities. At that point you can try several that sound interesting, until you find the one that works best for you.

Happy hunting!

Other resources available from
The 1687 Foundation

31 Days of Praise
by Ruth Myers
also available in Spanish.

Christians who long to experience God in a fresh, deeper way will treasure this powerful, personal praise guide. Every day for just one month, a Scripture-based devotion cultivates the "heart habit" of praise and worship. Readers will be amazed to discover how their lives can be *touched* and *changed* on a day-by-day, month-by-month basis. They will be gently inspired to appreciate and adore the Lord in all things—yes, even in the midst of pain, disappointment, and heartache. A deeper intimacy with God, and a greater love for Him, is the sure result. Come into His presence with praise.

31 Days of Prayer
by Ruth Myers,
also available in Spanish.

God invites us—*welcomes us*—into the high privilege of talking and working with Him. *31 Days of Prayer* shows you how to enjoy that privilege and begin an incredible prayer adventure. You'll discover in new ways that prayer is the slender nerve that moves the mighty hand of God. This is the perfect book to lead you in prayer for a full month—or many months—and help you create a prayer habit that lasts a lifetime. Rise above earthbound living...and into a new awareness of the Lord's delightful presence!

Karla Faye Tucker Set Free:
Life and Faith on Death Row
by Linda Strom

Karla Faye Tucker, the first woman executed in Texas in over one hundred years, became an evangelist for Christ during her fourteen-year imprisonment on Death Row. This is the story of Karla's spiritual journey, the women and men she reached, and the God who offers redemption and hope to the hardest of hearts.

Fruit Happens!
by Michael Christopher

Fruit happens when you spend time with God! *Fruit Happens!* also features one of the most exciting characters you might ever meet. His name is Dellie O'Shea, and his game is "over the top" in every possible way.

Dellie O'Shea is not someone who sits on the sidelines and watches the world pass by. He's a young man who puts his best instincts into action, especially those he gets directly from God. Along the way he learns what the "Fruits of the Spirit" are all about, by saving the life of another even as those same spiritual fruits grow and develop within himself.

He's also a Very Special Person in other ways as well—but you'll have to read his story to find out what they are!

Golden Turnabout
by Michael Christopher

Golden Turnabouts happen when you see with more than your eyes!

Golden Turnabout is the second in a series, featuring most of the same fascinating characters you've met before—including Dellie O'Shea! This time Dellie makes a new friend who seems to be slightly different from anyone else he's ever known. And maybe a little more prickly, too.

But things aren't always the way they first appear. Sometimes we judge a little too quickly, based on what we see on the outside before we have a chance to look a little deeper. And sometimes when we least expect it, others "do unto us" in ways that change our world for the better, even as Christ Himself would have us "do unto them."

Psalm 91: God's Umbrella of Protection
by Peggy Joyce Ruth
also available in Spanish.

Do the latest statistics on cancer, heart disease, and other medical conditions send a chill down your spine? Do thoughts of terrorist attacks and chemical warfare cause your heart to skip a beat? What about all the natural disasters that strike in unexpected places? Indeed—do you sometimes wonder if there is any safe haven anywhere in the world in which you might someday want to hide? If any of these things have ever troubled you, this can be one of the most important books you will ever read! In Psalm 91, the author's highly revealing, biblically based examination of the blessings God promises will open your heart, strengthen your spirit, and revitalize every aspect of your life!

Psalm 91: God's Shield of Protection (Military Edition)
by Peggy Joyce Ruth and Angelia Ruth Schum

Everything that's true about the "regular" edition of this book is also true of the Military Edition—only *more* so! This version is filled with military applications—almost every story has a military slant, and every testimonial comes from someone in the military who has *seen the God of Psalm 91 in action* in military situations, including combat. Many of these testimonials will astound and amaze you—God steps in again and again to protect His people and keep His promises. No situation is hopeless when God is in charge. This book proves it over and over again.

My Own Psalm 91
by Peggy Joyce Ruth
also available in Spanish

The Cross Pin
(shown mounted on card)

To request books or cross pins,
or for more information, please contact:
The 1687 Foundation
P.O. Box 1961
Sisters, OR 97759
Email: info@1687foundation.com
541.549.7600 tel
541.549.7603 fax